Dragon Hunt

First published in 2009
by Wayland

This paperback edition published in 2010

Text copyright © Karen Wallace 2009
Illustration copyright © Nigel Baines 2009

Wayland
338 Euston Road
London NW1 3BH

Wayland Australia
Level 17/207 Kent Street
Sydney, NSW 2000

Series Editor: Louise John
Cover design: Paul Cherrill
Design: D.R.ink
Consultant: Shirley Bickler

A CIP catalogue record for this book is available from the British Library.

ISBN 9780750256056 (hbk)
ISBN 9780750258173 (pbk)

Printed in China

Wayland is a division of Hachette Children's Books,
an Hachette UK Company

www.hachette.co.uk

Dragon Hunt

Written by Karen Wallace
Illustrated by Nigel Baines

WAYLAND

Princess PJ lived in a castle with her father, King Crusty, her mother, Queen Clementine and her brother, Prince Dandyfop.

Her real name was Penelope Josephine, but that was too girly for a tomboy princess, so she called herself PJ.

One day, King Crusty, who was very forgetful, made an announcement. "Uh…" he began.

"The king and the prince are going on a dragon hunt," declared Queen Clementine. "It's what kings and princes do."

"I HATE hunting dragons," cried Prince Dandyfop, who was as wet as a lettuce. "It's cold in the forest and I might catch a chill."

"Nonsense!" said his mother. "Do as you're told."

"I LOVE hunting dragons!" cried Princess PJ. "I'll go!"

"No," said Queen Clementine. "You are a princess. You will remain here and get dressed up for my tea party."

"I HATE tea parties!" cried Princess PJ.

"I'll stay," cried Prince Dandyfop.
"I'll wear my best velvet jacket."

Queen Clementine put her head in her hands. Sometimes everything seemed upside down.

The next day King Crusty went dragon-hunting with Prince Dandyfop.

When they arrived at the forest, they couldn't decide which way to go.

"It's getting dark," wailed Prince Dandyfop, "and I'm cold and wet."

There was the sound of beating hooves and a whoop of delight.

Princess PJ galloped up on her horse, swinging a dragon-catching net.

"Yippee," she shouted. "The palace is too cold for a tea party. I can join you after all!"

So Princess PJ set off with her father and brother.

They looked all day but they couldn't
see any sign of a dragon. There were
no burn marks on the trees and no
enormous footprints on the ground.

"I want to go home," whined Prince Dandyfop. "I'm catching a chill."
Princess PJ rolled her eyes at him.

"A nice fiery dragon will warm you up," she said, firmly. "Come and help me put up our tent."

Princess PJ and Prince Dandyfop set up camp.

King Crusty was already fast asleep.
He couldn't remember what he was out
hunting for anyway!

The next morning Princess PJ opened her eyes. She smelled smoke in the air.

"Wait here," she said to Prince Dandyfop,
who was hiding under his blanket.
"I'm going to find a dragon."

Princess PJ followed a trail of sooty prints and found the dragon in a cave. It had sharp teeth and flames shot out of its mouth.

"I'm not scared of you!" shouted Princess PJ. She got ready to swing her dragon-catching net.

But then a large tear rolled down the dragon's cheek.

"I'm so pleased to see you," he said. "I don't like living in this cave on my own."

Princess PJ had an idea.

"Would you like to come and heat up
our castle?" she asked the dragon.
"My mother and brother always
complain they are too cold."

So the dragon went home with Princess PJ. That winter, King Crusty's castle was the warmest in the land.

Queen Clementine gave lots of parties and Prince Dandyfop never caught a chill again!

START READING is a series of highly enjoyable books for beginner readers. **The books have been carefully graded to match the Book Bands widely used in schools.** This enables readers to be sure they choose books that match their own reading ability.

Look out for the Band colour on the book in our Start Reading logo.

The Bands are:

	Pink Band 1
	Red Band 2
	Yellow Band 3
	Blue Band 4
	Green Band 5
	Orange Band 6
	Turquoise Band 7
	Purple Band 8
	Gold Band 9

START READING books can be read independently or shared with an adult. They promote the enjoyment of reading through satisfying stories supported by fun illustrations.

Karen Wallace was brought up in a log cabin in Canada. She has written lots of different books for children and even won a few awards. Karen likes writing funny books because she can laugh at her own jokes! She has two sons and two cats.

Nigel Baines lives in St. Albans. He has illustrated lots of books for children, including some about a little boy who likes to burp and pick his nose! He had lots of fun drawing PJ's dragon and hopes you'll enjoy reading about it, too.